Skills Builders

Spelling and Vocabulary

YEAR
6

Brenda Stones

RISING STARS

Rising Stars UK Ltd, 7 Hatchers Mews, Bermondsey Street, London SE1 3GS
www.risingstars-uk.com

Every effort has been made to trace copyright holders and obtain their permission for the use of copyright materials. The publishers will gladly receive information enabling them to rectify any error or omission in subsequent editions.

All facts are correct at time of going to press.

Published 2013
Reprinted with revisions 2014
Text, design and layout © 2013 Rising Stars UK Ltd

Project manager: Dawn Booth
Editorial: David Hemsley
Proofreader: Claire Shewbridge, Denise Moulton
Design: Words & Pictures, London
Cover design: Amina Dudhia
Acknowledgement: p.36 *Collins Junior Illustrated Thesaurus* © HarperCollins Publishers 2005, 2010; p.46 illustrations by Dave Thompson

British Library Cataloguing-in-Publication Data
A CIP record for this book is available from the British Library.

ISBN: 978-0-85769-702-8
Printed in Singapore by Craftprint International Limited

Contents

4   How to use this book

6   Revise words ending in -sure and -ture

7   Revise words ending with a shun sound

8   Revise spelling rules

9   Revise comparatives and superlatives

10 More prefixes

12 Foreign plurals, foreign suffixes

14 Suffix -ance, -ence

16 Suffix -ery, -ory, -ary

18 Revise suffix -le, -el, -al

20 Revise suffix -er, -or, -ar

22 Vocabulary: antonyms

24 Spelling rule: i before e

26 Revise stress in words

28 Silent syllables

30 Making verbs

32 Making nouns

34 Vocabulary: synonyms

36 Using a thesaurus

38 Homophones

40 Informal and formal vocabulary

42 Vocabulary: standard English

43 Idioms and colloquialisms

44 Word list for Years 5 and 6

45 The Spelling Test

46 Vocabulary: compound words

47 Answers (may be detached)

How to use this book

The content and sequence of this series of Skills Builders on Spelling and Vocabulary are closely based on the revised National Curriculum for English.

Provided within this book:

1 Active teaching of individual spelling rules.

2 Emphasis on regular patterns in English spelling.

3 Writing grids to reinforce these spelling patterns.

4 Spelling jars and pots in which children make collections of common spellings.

5 Thematic vocabulary pages.

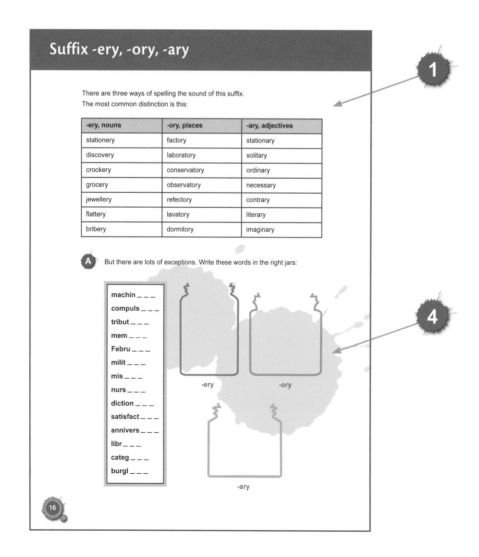

How to use this book

6 Occasional testing through dictation and word lists.

7 Two or three practical exercises for each section that progress in difficulty.

8 A variety of layouts to help prepare for the GPS tests.

9 Encouragement of individual research in dictionaries and online.

10 Some more imaginative exercises on rhyme and alphabets.

11 'How did I do?' checks for self-evaluation.

12 Answers in a cut-out section for self-checking.

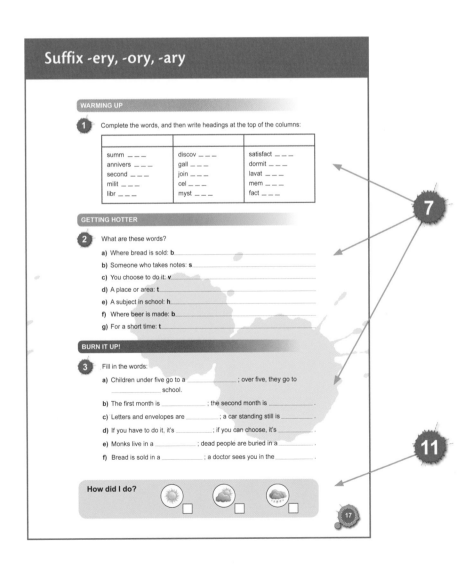

Revise words ending in -sure and -ture

You will need to learn which ending to use, **-sure** (measure) or **-ture** (mixture).

1 Add **-sure** or **-ture** to complete each of the following words:

a) mea _____   b) punc _____

c) na _____   d) in _____

e) enclo _____   f) crea _____

g) plea _____   h) adven _____

i) fu _____   j) trea _____

k) un _____   l) frac _____

GETTING HOTTER

2 Choose the correct ending and sort the following words into the correct jars:

fixsure	**fixture**
composure	**compoture**
feasure	**feature**
vulture	**vulsure**
leiture	**leisure**
strucsure	**structure**
picture	**picsure**
exposure	**exposture**
gesture	**gesure**

-sure

-ture

How did I do?

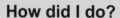

Revise words ending with a shun sound

In Year 6, it is important that you can recap spelling rules. One of the most difficult rules to remember is how to spell the ending that sounds like **shun**.

The four most common ways to make this ending are:

tion	sion	ssion	cian
tradition	tension	mission	magician (usually used when spelling professions)

(**-cean** is also used in ocean and **-cheon** in truncheon)

WARMING UP

 1   Add **-tion**, **-sion**, **-ssion** or **-cian** to complete the following words:

a) beauti _____

b) competi _____

c) ten _____

d) educa _____

e) conclu _____

f) techni _____

g) subtrac _____

h) musi _____

GETTING HOTTER

2   Circle the words that are spelt incorrectly. Write the correct spelling of each word on the lines:

fracsion	percussion	
admission	creacian	
decision	suspician	
pention	coversasion	
politition	attenshun	
pollution		

How did I do?

 ☐   ☐   ☐

Revise spelling rules

Here are three rules to remember when spelling confusing words.

Words that contain qu

The letter **q** is nearly always followed by the letter **u**.

q + u = qu, for example: **queen**

A   Add **qu** to the following words and remember the pattern:

i) .... ery   ii) .... estion

iii) re............... est   iv) fre............... ent

v) ac............... aint   vi) e............... al

vii) dis............... alify   viii) en............... iry

ix) earth............... ake   x) tur............... oise

xi) s............... irrel   xii) .... iz

xiii) .... ick   xiv) li............... id

Be careful, as some words that end in **que** sound as if they end in **k**, for example:

| opaque | antique | cheque | unique |

Soft c sounds like an s

Soft **c** sounds like an **s** but is written as **c**.
Soft **c** comes before: **e** in suc**c**eed, **i** in **c**ircle, **y** in litera**c**y.

B   Add a **c** to the following words and learn the rule:

i) .... yclist   ii) .... ircus

iii) prin............... ess   iv) .... ity

v) dan............... e   vi) poli............... e

vii) .... ylinder   viii) .... ymbals

ix) spi............... y   x) vacan............... y

xi) jui............... y   xii) ra............... ism

gue endings have a silent ue

You will need to learn this rule because, in most words that end with **gue**, the **ue** is silent. For example: ton**gue**. The exception to this rule is the word **argue**.

C   Add **gue** to the following words:

i) pla...............   ii) lea...............

iii) catalo...............   iv) dialo...............

v) va...............   vi) intri...............

vii) collea...............   viii) vo...............

Revise comparatives and superlatives

Comparatives and superlatives are adjectives that compare two or more things – and can say how super they are!

The comparative compares two things and usually ends in **-er** or uses the word **more**.

For example: The car is smaller than the bus.

The superlative compares three or more things and usually ends in **-est** or uses the word **most**.

For example: The candle is bright, the torch is brighter, but the lamp is the brightest.

Be careful when spelling irregular adjectives:

Descriptor	Comparative form	Superlative form
good	better	best
bad	worse	worst
far	farther/further	farthest/furthest
little	less	least
many	more	most

WARMING UP

 1 Complete this table:

Descriptor	Comparative form	Superlative form
big	bigger	biggest
tall		
	angrier	
mean		
		darkest
		longest
	harder	

GETTING HOTTER

 2 Complete the words in these sentences by writing in the missing letters:

a) Nadien is the slow............... runner in our team. I can run much fast...............
than him.

b) My dad and uncle are young............... than my mum. She is the old...............

c) Claire's bag is light............... than mine, but Faye's bag is the heav...............

d) The blue trainers are cheap but the green ones are cheap...............

How did I do? ☐ ☐ ☐

More prefixes

Here are more prefixes, from Latin and Greek.

Prefix	Meaning	Sample words
ambi	both	ambidextrous, ambiguous
audi	hearing	audible, audience
contra	against	contradict, contrast
extra	outside	extraordinary, extramural
fore	before	foretaste, forehead
hyper	extra	hyperactive, hypermarket
micro	small	microchip, microscope
mono	only	monopoly, monorail
octo	eight	octopus, octagon
omni	all	omnibus, omnivorous
photo	light	photograph, photosynthesis
prime	first	primary, primrose
tele	distant	television, telephone

 A   Add more words for each prefix, using your dictionary.

More prefixes

1 Write the word for:

a) predicting the weather: fore..

b) very critical: hyper..

c) sensitive to light: photo..

d) smuggling goods: contra..

e) test which is heard: audi..

f) married to one person: mono..

2 Can you give the exact meaning of the parts of these words? The first has been done for you:

a) extra + mural   *outside the walls*   = *outside normal bounds*

b) tele + vision ....   = ...

c) di + lapidated ....   = ...

d) ambi + dextrous ....   = ...

e) omni + potent ....   = ...

f) tele + scope ....   = ...

3 Make new words using the prefixes on the opposite page, e.g.

octodextrous = having eight hands

....

....

....

....

How did I do?

 ☐   ☐   ☐

Foreign plurals, foreign suffixes

When you make plurals of words with foreign endings, you follow their rules for plural endings.

Singular	Ending	Plural	Language
cactus, stimulus	i	cacti, stimuli	Latin
formula, larva	ae	formulae, larvae	Latin
medium, datum	a	media, data	Latin
gateau, chateau	x	gateaux, chateaux	French
criterion	a	criteria	Greek

A Add more examples to the table above as you find them.

There are also several Greek suffixes that help us make new words:

Suffix	Meaning	Sample words
graph	writing	autograph, paragraph
phobia	fear	claustrophobia, agoraphobia
logy	study	biology, zoology
scope	look	telescope, microscope

B Add more examples to the table above as you find them.

Foreign plurals, foreign suffixes

1 Give the plural of:

a) terminus ....

b) plateau ....

c) tumulus ....

d) antenna ....

e) stadium ....

f) addendum ....

2 Give the meaning of these words:

a) micro + scope .... = ...

b) photo + graph .... = ...

c) auto + graph .... = ...

d) omni + phobia .... = ...

e) crimin + ology .... = ...

3 a) If *kallos* means beauty, what does **calligraphy** mean?

....

b) And what does **kaleidoscope** mean?

....

c) If *hydra* means water, what does **hydrophobia** mean?

....

d) And if *arakhne* means spider, what is **arachnophobia**?

....

How did I do?

 ☐   ☐   ☐

Suffix -ance, -ence

These noun suffixes are linked to the adjective suffixes **-ant** and **-ent**.

 A Fill in the nouns:

Adjective	Noun
tolerant	tolerance
ignorant	
abundant	
resonant	
ascendant	
attendant	
brilliant	
compliant	

Adjective	Noun
obedient	obedience
confident	
decadent	
coherent	
indulgent	
convergent	
divergent	
emergent	

The **-ant** suffix is often used for people, even if the abstract noun ends in **-ence**:

Person	Noun
defendant	defence
confidant	confidence
descendant	descent

Suffix -ance, -ence

 1 Add **-ance** or **-ence** endings and then write headings at the top of the columns:

reluct...........	insol...........
eleg...........	innoc...........
fragr...........	recurr...........
assist...........	differ...........
reli...........	excell...........
arrog...........	pres...........
signific...........	prud...........
attend...........	compet...........
const...........	pati...........
repugn...........	dilig...........

GETTING HOTTER

 2 Give the word for a person:

a) in combat ....

b) who communicates ....

c) who defends ....

d) who descends from a family ....

e) who applies for a job ....

f) who is in dispute ....

BURN IT UP!

 3 Choose the right words for the gaps.

a) I am .... on my oldest .... **(dependent / dependant)**

b) We need an .... to be in .... **(attendance / attendant)**

c) We've had one .... enter the ....
(correspondence / respondent)

d) My best .... tells me everything in ....
(confidence / confidant)

e) The .... in the case is speaking in his own ....
(defendant / defence)

How did I do?   ☐   ☐   ☐

Suffix -ery, -ory, -ary

There are three ways of spelling the sound of this suffix.
The most common distinction is this:

-ery, nouns	-ory, places	-ary, adjectives
stationery	factory	stationary
discovery	laboratory	solitary
crockery	conservatory	ordinary
grocery	observatory	necessary
jewellery	refectory	contrary
flattery	lavatory	literary
bribery	dormitory	imaginary

 A But there are lots of exceptions. Write these words in the right jars:

machin _ _ _

compuls _ _ _

tribut _ _ _

mem _ _ _

Febru _ _ _

milit _ _ _

mis _ _ _

nurs _ _ _

diction _ _ _

satisfact _ _ _

annivers _ _ _

libr _ _ _

categ _ _ _

burgl _ _ _

-ery

-ory

-ary

Suffix -ery, -ory, -ary

1 Complete the words, and then write headings at the top of the columns:

summ _ _ _	discov _ _ _	satisfact _ _ _
annivers _ _ _	gall _ _ _	dormit _ _ _
second _ _ _	join _ _ _	lavat _ _ _
milit _ _ _	cel _ _ _	mem _ _ _
libr _ _ _	myst _ _ _	fact _ _ _

GETTING HOTTER

2 What are these words?

a) Where bread is sold: **b**

b) Someone who takes notes: **s**

c) You choose to do it: **v**

d) A place or area: **t**

e) A subject in school: **h**

f) Where beer is made: **b**

g) For a short time: **t**

BURN IT UP!

3 Fill in the words:

a) Children under five go to a .... ; over five, they go to .... school.

b) The first month is .... ; the second month is ....

c) Letters and envelopes are .... ; a car standing still is ....

d) If you have to do it, it's .... ; if you can choose, it's ....

e) Monks live in a .... ; dead people are buried in a ....

f) Bread is sold in a .... ; a doctor sees you in the ....

How did I do?

 ☐   ☐   ☐

Revise suffix -le, -el, -al

You learned the **-le** ending earlier, but let's compare the other spellings for this **-ul** sound:

-le	-el	-al	-il	-ol	-ul
battle	label	normal	pencil	idol	careful
cuddle	satchel	special	stencil	pistol	helpful
settle	rebel	partial	pupil		hopeful
piffle	camel	medal			handful
castle	parcel	sandal			
sparkle	squirrel	petal			
adorable	vessel	pedal			
dependable	tunnel	animal			
invisible	funnel	crystal			

-le: the most common ending, used for three groups of words:

- the double consonant pattern after a short vowel

- after a long vowel, such as **table**, or multiple consonants, as in **thistle**

- in the suffix **-able** and **-ible**

-el: far less common, but including:

- after double **n**, **r**, **s**

-al: more common in adjectives, including the **-ial** pattern; but also for several individual nouns

-il: less common, and mainly for nouns

-ol: a rare ending, for nouns

-ul: all the many words that end **-ful**

 Can you find more words ending **-il** and **-ol**?
Add them to the columns above.

Revise suffix -le, -el, -al

1 Complete the words, and then write headings at the top of the columns:

decim __ __	amiab __ __	reb __ __
cannib __ __	pudd __ __	tass __ __
scand __ __	pimp __ __	pan __ __
rasc __ __	tentac __ __	barr __ __
ped __ __	crad __ __	tunn __ __

2 Can you spell these words ending with the **-ul** sound?

a) between your leg and your foot ....

b) when you argue ....

c) where you go when you're ill ....

d) a green leaf that stings ....

e) it has two wheels ....

f) it has humps ....

g) enough to fill a cup ....

3 Choose the right words to fill the gaps:

a) He may be my .... but he is very .... (idle / idol)

b) The .... party walked along the .... path. (bridle / bridal)

c) The .... reason I'm leaving is a question of ....
(principle / principal)

d) Don't .... with my gold .... (medal / meddle)

e) I don't eat .... , but I do have strong ....
(muscles / mussels)

How did I do?

 ☐   ☐   ☐

Revise suffix -er, -or, -ar

Here is another common suffix sound that can be spelt in several ways:

-er	-or	-ar	-a	-our	-re
baker	doctor	beggar	camera	flavour	metre
butcher	editor	vicar	comma	odour	mitre
hammer	sailor	cellar	panda	harbour	centre
butter	author	collar	banana	honour	theatre
letter	calculator	grammar	cinema	labour	massacre
river	mayor	calendar	opera	humour	manoeuvre
teacher	tailor	vinegar	pyjama	vapour	

These examples are all nouns.

-er: the most common ending; also used for comparative adjectives

-or: especially used for people's jobs

-a: this ending usually comes from foreign origins

-our and **-re** are both spelt differently in American English: **-or** and **-er**

A **i)** How do you spell the **-our** words when you add a suffix?

e.g. honour + able = ... ;

vigour + ous = ...

ii) How do you spell the **-re** words when you add a suffix?

e.g. metre + ical = ... ;

theatre + ical = ...

Revise suffix -er, -or, -ar

WARMING UP

1 Join the letters to the endings to make words:

bak	
hamm	er
trait	
burgl	
begg	ar
vict	
maj	
riv	or
pill	

GETTING HOTTER

2 What is the word for:

a) A farm machine: **t**...

b) Person in the theatre: **a**...

c) American money: **d**...

d) For example, red or green: **c**...

e) What knights wear: **a**...

f) Someone visiting: **v**...

g) Sells meat: **b**...

BURN IT UP!

3 Choose the right words for the gaps in the sentences.

a) A .... digs coal; mining is now a .... industry. (**miner / minor**)

b) The .... is used by a .... of wine. (**seller / cellar**)

c) Planes are kept in a .... and clothes on a ....
(**hanger / hangar**)

d) A .... is like a monk, but a .... makes chips. (**fryer / friar**)

e) A .... runs a census, but a .... senses movement.
(**sensor / censor**)

How did I do?

 ☐   ☐   ☐

Vocabulary: antonyms

Antonyms are words that mean the opposite of another word.

 A Do you remember how to make an antonym using prefixes?
Write the antonym of the following:

Prefix	Root	Antonym
un-	able	
de-	frost	
dis-	taste	
mis-	place	
anti-	clockwise	
non-	sense	
in-	capable	

When the prefix **in-** comes before certain consonants, it changes its spelling:

Prefix	Before	Becomes	Sample words
in-	l	ill	illegal
in-	m	imm	immature
in-	r	irr	irregular
in-	p	imp	imperfect
in-	b	imb	imbalance

B Another way of making antonyms is to add the suffix **-less**.
Write the antonym of these words:

i) hope

ii) care

iii) mind

iv) top

v) clue

vi) fat

Vocabulary: antonyms

1 Write the meanings of these different antonyms:

a) anti-smoker

b) non-smoker

c) ex-smoker

....

....

....

d) displace

e) misplace

f) replace

....

....

....

2 Match pairs of antonyms:

crouch
lose
blacken
uninterested
disinterested
steam
solidify
strengthen
rapidly

fascinated
weaken
liquefy
biased
sluggishly
find
leap
whiten
ice

3 Write antonyms for these words:

a) brilliant ....

b) maximum ....

c) boiling ....

d) suddenly ....

e) proud ....

f) athlete ....

g) ceiling ....

How did I do?

 ☐

 ☐

 ☐

23

Spelling rule: i before e

There is a spelling rule that says 'i before e except after c'.

Here are the most common examples, for the sound **ee**:

i before e	Except after c	Exceptions
hankerchief	ceiling	seize
relief	deceive, deceit	protein
belief	conceive, conceit	caffeine
siege	receive, receipt	
piece	perceive	
niece		
shield		
shriek		

Note that awkward p in receipt!

When the sound is not **ee**, there are more variations:

ie as long i	ie as two syllables	ei as 'ay'	ei as long i	ei as 'air'
lie	science	vein	either	their
die	glacier	veil	neither	heir
pie	happier	rein	height	
tie	medieval	reign		
tied	quiet	weigh		
ties	fiery	eight		

Spelling rule: i before e

WARMING UP

1 Join pairs of rhyming words:

receipt
conceive
their
tied
either
chief
fierce
patient
yield

neither
pierce
field
ancient
heir
perceive
thief
cried
deceit

GETTING HOTTER

2 Join the rhyming pairs; this time the vowel sounds are spelt differently:

pieced
grief
eight
reign
pier
view
friend
field
their

pealed
state
mare
new
bend
stain
fear
leaf
priest

BURN IT UP!

3 Find words from the opposite page to complete the sentences:

a) My brother's daughter is my ....

b) I blow my nose in a cotton ....

c) The top of a room is its ....

d) When I buy something, I'm given a ....

e) The number after seven is ....

f) How tall I am is my ....

g) A town being attacked could be under ....

How did I do?

 ☐   ☐   ☐

25

Revise stress in words

Do you remember this rule about adding suffixes to words with more than one syllable?

If the stress is on the last syllable, you double the last letter if it's a single consonant after a short vowel sound:

forget	forgetting, forgotten
regret	regretted, regretting
forbid	forbidding, forbidden
omit	omitted, omitting, omission
commit	committed, committal, committing
permit	permitted, permitting, permission
abet	abetted, abetting
fulfil	fulfilled, fulfilling

If the stress is on an earlier syllable, you only double the last consonant if it's l:

cancel	cancelled, cancelling
label	labelled, labelling
signal	signalled, signalling
quarrel	quarrelled, quarrelling
enter	entered, entering
offer	offered, offering
open	opener, opened, opening
abandon	abandoned, abandoning
spirit	spirited, dispirited
limit	limited, limiting
benefit	benefited, benefiting

With these verbs, you double or not, according to where the stress lies:

Verb	Stress on first syllable	Stress on second syllable
refer	reference, referee	referred, referral, referring
prefer	preference	preferred, preferring
transfer	transference	transferred, transferring

Revise stress in words

1 Write these verbs in the past tense. The first has been done for you:

gallop	galloped
forget	
forbid	
cancel	
travel	
signal	
trumpet	
level	
visit	

GETTING HOTTER

2 Write the nouns from these verbs. The first has been done for you:

refer	reference
transfer	
begin	
cancel	
abandon	
limit	
permit	
prefer	

BURN IT UP!

3 Write these verbs in the sentences, with the correct spelling for the verb endings (**-ed** or **-ing**):

a) I _____ the milk before _____ my aunt. (**cancel / visit**)

b) He _____ that I should not be _____ . (**signal / travel**)

c) The horse _____ away, _____ its rider. (**gallop / abandon**)

d) When I _____ the room, I _____ to the list. (**enter / refer**)

e) I _____ what I had _____ . (**regret / forget**)

f) I _____ it before _____ it up. (**label / parcel**)

How did I do?

27

Silent syllables

As we speak faster than we write, some syllables remain in spelling but are lost in speech.

They are usually the unstressed syllables.

 A How do you say these words?

Full spelling	Spoken syllables	Missing letters
Wednesday	2	d, e
chocolates		
lavatory		
secretary		
extraordinary		
comfortable		
temperature		
literature		
interesting		
every		
valuable		
sovereign		

Pronunciation varies in different regions, so you may say words in different ways from other people.

Silent syllables

WARMING UP

1 Match words with the same number of **written** syllables:

review
weird
bone
observatory
diamonds
comfortable
extraordinary

chocolates
late
indefatigable
secretary
pierce
ancient
laboratory

GETTING HOTTER

2 Write the whole words, supplying the missing letters:

a) parl_____ment ....

b) val_____ble ....

c) d_____monds ....

d) Feb_____ry ....

e) gov_____ment ....

f) anc_____nt ....

g) sc_____nce ....

h) myst_____ry ....

BURN IT UP!

3 Write these words, which all have silent syllables:

					a				
Greens you eat					a				
Where a scientist works					a				
Adjective from decorate					a				
Houses of P_____					a				
Normally					a				

How did I do?

Making verbs

When you turn one word class into another, you often add a suffix.
These are common suffixes for verbs:

-en	-ise	-ify	-ate
harden	liquidise	glorify	annotate
loosen	vaporise	horrify	enumerate
dampen	harmonise	terrify	confiscate
deepen	organise	notify	decimate
deafen	apologise	clarify	abdicate
fatten	advertise	justify	formulate

 A Work out the root word for each of the verbs above, and write its word class under these headings:

-en	-ise	-ify	-ate

With these particular examples:

-en is added to adjectives

-ise is added to nouns

-ify is added to nouns

-ate is for original verbs, which are themselves root words.

Making verbs

 1 Use suffixes to turn these adjectives into verbs
(remember your spelling rules):

less		black	
fat		white	
red		broad	
coarse		wide	
cheap		quick	

 2 Use suffixes to turn these nouns into verbs:

colony		theory	
demon		beauty	
digit		class	
energy		identity	
motor		quantity	
television			

 3 **a)** Turn these adjectives into verbs, using a variety of suffixes:

equal		local	
moral		maximum	
simple		minimum	
solid		pure	

b) And when liquid becomes a verb, it can have three different endings:

_____ _____ _____

How did I do?   ☐   ☐   ☐

31

Making nouns

When you make nouns out of other root words, you can also add suffixes. These are common suffixes for noun endings:

-ness	-ility	-ism	-tion
hardness	capability	pacifism	annotation
looseness	suitability	militarism	enumeration
dampness	probability	classicism	confiscation
deepness	possibility	romanticism	addition
deafness	visibility	autism	definition
thinness	credibility	feminism	position

 A Again, write the word class of each of the root words under the noun endings:

-ness	-ility	-ism	-tion

Your findings are probably:

-ness is added to adjectives to make nouns

-ility is added to **-able** and **-ible** adjectives, and retains the root of those spellings

-ism is added to adjectives to make words that describe beliefs or symptoms

-tion is often added to verbs, and echoes their original spelling.

Making nouns

WARMING UP

1 Turn these adjectives into nouns:

fat	
red	
coarse	
cheap	

black	
white	
quick	

GETTING HOTTER

2 Turn these adjectives into nouns (and watch your spelling):

flexible	
vulnerable	
sensible	
changeable	

feasible	
enjoyable	
legible	
reliable	

BURN IT UP!

3 These signs all have names that end with the **-shun** sound.
Write the names, and then find the one whose spelling is different from the others:

\+ ....

\– ....

× ....

÷ ....

$\frac{1}{2}$ or $\frac{1}{4}$ or $\frac{1}{3}$ ....

? .... mark

! .... mark

How did I do?

 ☐   ☐   ☐

33

Vocabulary: synonyms

To build a larger vocabulary, it's good to think of different, more unusual words to use.

 In each brick of this wall, write an alternative word or words to mean roughly the same.

Do use a dictionary or thesaurus!

shiny	tall	jagged	soft	sharp
plodding	crawling	racing	leaping	
said	shouted	whispered	announced	replied
slowly	loudly	suddenly	quietly	
near	beside	below	above	behind
thief	granny	assistant	official	

You'll see that each row was a different word class. Name them.

....

....

....

....

Vocabulary: synonyms

 1 Match pairs of synonyms:

darting	quietly
brilliantly	deafening
hard	dozing
softly	plodding
loud	racing
snoozing	harsh
trudging	wonderfully

GETTING HOTTER

 2 Write three words to bridge each of these gaps. The first has been done for you.

a) freezing   *cool*   *tepid*   *hot*   baking

b) dawdling   racing

c) tiny   gigantic

d) stupid   clever

e) starving   bursting

BURN IT UP!

 3 Choose the most appropriate word for each gap:

a) The hospital welcomes .
   (**patients / invalids / customers**)

b) The buses are full of .
   (**grandparents / pensioners / ancestors**)

c) The football club is proud of its .
   (**supporters / adolescents / teenagers**)

d) Mothers cradle their .
   (**toddlers / infants / babies**)

e) You will be served by .
   (**defendants / assistants / supervisors**)

How did I do? ☐ ☐ ☐

Using a thesaurus

Here is a page from the *Collins Junior Thesaurus*:

believe VERB
If you **believe** someone or something, you think what is said is true.

accept
She can't **accept** that she is wrong.

trust
I **trusted** him, but it seems he was not telling the truth.

bend (1) VERB
When something **bends**, it becomes curved or crooked.

buckle
Her bike hit a rock that badly **buckled** the front wheel.

fold
The blacksmith heated a strip of iron and **folded** it in half.

twist
A man **twisted** long balloons into the shape of an animal.

bend (2) NOUN
A **bend** is a curve in something.

corner
The house you are looking for is round the next **corner**.

curve
Round a **curve** in the river was the waterfall where we ate our picnic.

loop
Loops in the mountain road made the drive scary.

bend (3) VERB
When you **bend**, you move your body forwards and downwards.

bow
The farmer **bowed** his back under a heavy sack of oats.

crouch
We **crouched** down out of sight.

lean
Sam **leaned** over and stroked the kitten.

stoop
Stooping down, she touched the track made by the deer.

better (1) ADJECTIVE
Something that is **better** than something else is of a higher standard or quality.

finer
I couldn't have had a **finer** teacher.

greater
After all his study, he had a **greater** understanding of the subject.

better (2) ADJECTIVE
If you are feeling **better** after an illness, you are not feeling so ill.

healthier
Sean certainly looks much **healthier** now.

recovering
Grandma had a nasty fall but she is now **recovering**.

stronger
I felt really weak, but I'm getting **stronger** every day.

a
Bb
c
d
e
f
g
h
i
j
k
l
m
n
o
p
q
r
s
t
u
v
w
x
y
z

15

Using a thesaurus

1 Describe the type styles used for:

a) main headwords

b) word classes

c) synonyms

d) definitions

e) sample sentences

GETTING HOTTER

2 How many headwords are there for each word class?

a) nouns

b) verbs

c) adjectives

d) Why do you think that is?

BURN IT UP!

3 **a)** Take the three synonyms for **bend (1)** and write them in increasing order of intensity:

b) Take the four synonyms for **bend (3)** and do the same:

c) Why is **bend** given three separate numbers?

d) What synonyms could you write for **belief** (NOUN)?

e) What synonyms could you write for **better** (ADVERB)?

How did I do?

Homophones

You know that homophones are words that sound the same but mean different things.

Often they are different word classes.

 A   Write which ones are different below. The first has been done for you:

bold / bowled   *adjective / verb*

break / brake

ceiling / sealing

draft / draught

find / fined

guilt / gilt

heart / hart

horde / hoard

it's / its

knead / need

lava / larva

law / lore

miner / minor

muscle / mussel

medal / meddle

pedal / peddle

place / plaice

profit / prophet

root / route

rough / ruff

sauce / source

sort / sought

throne / thrown

waste / waist

Homophones

WARMING UP

 1 Write a sample sentence for each of these:

    a) passed as a verb _____

    b) past as a noun _____

    c) past as an adjective _____

    d) past as a preposition _____

    e) past as an adverb _____

GETTING HOTTER

 2 Write sample sentences for:

    a) fast as an adjective _____

    b) fast as a verb _____

    c) fast as an adverb _____

    d) less as an adjective _____

    e) less as an adverb _____

    f) lesser as an adjective _____

BURN IT UP!

 3 Write sample sentences for:

    a) compliment as a noun _____

    b) compliment as a verb _____

    c) complement as a noun _____

    d) complement as a verb _____

How did I do?

Informal and formal vocabulary

The English National Curriculum emphasises how vocabulary changes by context:

- in informal speech
- for formal speech and writing.

 Make notes below on the different **occasions** when you use formal or informal language; the different **audiences** you are speaking or writing to; and examples of the different **language** you use in those situations:

	Informal	Formal
Occasions		
Audience		
Examples of language		

Informal and formal vocabulary

WARMING UP

 1 Make a list of texting phrases, which you use informally. The first has been done for you:

wud _what you doing?_

GETTING HOTTER

 2 In formal language, contractions are less acceptable.
Spell these out in full:

a) shouldn't

b) mustn't

c) won't

d) shan't

e) we'll

f) he'd

BURN IT UP!

 3 Match these informal and formal words by meaning:

said
then
love from

alleged
yours sincerely
subsequently
claimed
yours faithfully
thereafter
reported
consequently
reckoned

How did I do?

Vocabulary: standard English

Standard English is formal English.

Using I and me correctly

If you are unsure whether to use **I** or **me** in your writing, check by saying the sentence in the first person singular, for example:

The teacher asked Emma and _____ to tidy the book area.
The teacher asked (I or me) to tidy the book area.
The teacher asked me to tidy the book area.
The teacher asked Emma and <u>me</u> to tidy the book area.

A Add **I** or **me** to complete these sentences correctly:

    i) Dad told Luke and_____ to pick up the toys.

    ii) Alex, Salim and_____ got through to the art final.

    iii) Marta handed her homework in but Natalia and_____ didn't.

    iv) Mum and_____ forgot to buy Gran's birthday present.

Writing words in full

Avoid using contractions and abbreviations when you are writing in a formal situation.

B Write these contractions in full:

    i) they're_____   **ii)** shan't _____

    iii) gr8 _____   **iv)** & _____

    v) ave _____   **vi)** min _____

    vii) max _____   **viii)** anon _____

Double negatives

If there are two negatives in a sentence, the literal translation makes the sentence positive. For example, 'He didn't break nothing' means that he did break something!

C Rewrite these sentences using just **one** negative.

    i) I didn't see nobody at the park.

    _____

    ii) I don't want nothing from the shop.

    _____

    iii) She can't make friends with nobody.

    _____

    iv) Make sure you don't get into no trouble.

    _____

Idioms and colloquialisms

Remind yourself what idioms and colloquialisms are.

Idioms are when words do not mean what they say, for example, 'It cost an arm and a leg', meaning it was very expensive.

Colloquialisms are words and phrases that are informal, for example, 'well good', 'kind of' and 'pretty quick'.

A Write the meaning of these clauses and phrases in standard English:

i) shake a leg _____

ii) sort of _____

iii) have your heart set on it _____

iv) chip on shoulder _____

v) best of both worlds _____

vi) apple of my eye _____

vii) cross your fingers _____

viii) drive someone up the wall _____

ix) let the cat out of the bag _____

x) no room to swing a cat _____

xi) put a sock in it _____

B Rewrite this text in standard English:

> We were supposed to be going to stretch our legs but it was raining cats and dogs so we decided to stay inside instead. I was kind of gutted and said I hoped the weather would improve. But Dad said, 'There's more chance of pigs flying!'

_____

_____

_____

_____

_____

_____

Word list for Years 5 and 6

These are some of the words that you are expected to understand and spell in Year 6.

 1 Practise writing and spelling the following words:

Word	Look	Cover	Say	Check
amateur				
foreign				
lightning				
individual				
persuade				
yacht				
symbol				
bruise				
excellent				

GETTING HOTTER

2 Underline the word that is spelt correctly:

haras	harass	harrass
occupy	occupie	ocupy
stomack	stomac	stomach
achieeve	achieve	acheive
professhun	professian	profession
reconise	recognyse	recognise
community	communitey	comunity
pregidice	prejudice	prejudis

BURN IT UP!

3 Use each word in a sentence:

a) signature _____

b) recommend _____

c) according _____

d) privilege _____

How did I do?

 ☐   ☐   ☐

44

The Spelling Test

WARMING UP

1 How many syllables are there in each of these words?

    a) hippopotamus

    b) necessarily

    c) beneficial

    d) incidentally

    e) scientifically

    f) elephantine

GETTING HOTTER

2 Ring the errors and rewrite correctly underneath:

> I've been benefitting from traveling around the circumference of the gloab: I've visitted meny counties in Europe, and crosed many briges. Now Im back home and puting my feet up by the harth.

BURN IT UP!

3 Write as many synonyms as you can think of for:

    a) hot

    b) cold

    c) wet

    d) dry

How did I do?

Vocabulary: compound words

A **compound word** is made when two words are joined to create a new word.

Use a thesaurus to acquire new vocabulary – how many compound words can you find in your thesaurus?

WARMING UP

 1 Use the pictures to write the compound words:

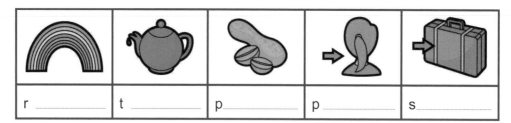

r _____ t _____ p _____ p _____ s _____

GETTING HOTTER

2 Use a word from Jar 1 and join it with a word from Jar 2 to make a compound word:

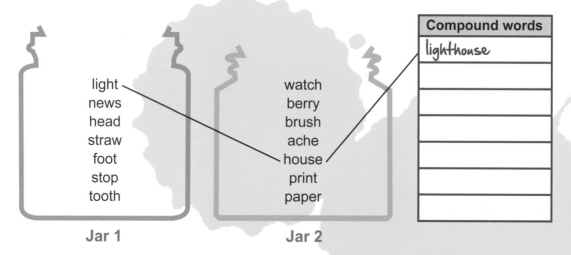

Compound words
lighthouse

light
news
head
straw
foot
stop
tooth

Jar 1

watch
berry
brush
ache
house
print
paper

Jar 2

BURN IT UP!

3 Use each compound word in a sentence:

a) countryside _____

b) throughout _____

c) themselves _____

d) headquarters _____

How did I do?

 ☐   ☐   ☐

 46

Answers

Revise words ending in -sure and -ture (page 6)

1 a) measure b) puncture c) nature d) insure e) enclosure f) creature
g) pleasure h) adventure i) future j) treasure k) unsure l) fracture

2 -sure: composure, leisure, exposure
-ture: fixture, feature, vulture, structure, picture, gesture

Revise words ending with a shun sound (page 7)

1 a) beautician b) competition c) tension d) education e) conclusion
f) technician g) subtraction h) musician

2

(fracsion) admission	percussion	fraction
decision	(creacian)	creation
(pention)	(suspician)	suspicion
(politition)	(coversasion)	pension
pollution	(attenshun)	conversation
		politician
		attention

Revise spelling rules (page 8)

A i) query ii) question iii) request iv) frequent v) acquaint vi) equal
vii) disqualify viii) enquiry ix) earthquake x) turquoise xi) squirrel
xii) quiz xiii) quick xiv) liquid

B i) cyclist ii) circus iii) princess iv) city v) dance vi) police
vii) cylinder viii) cymbals ix) spicy x) vacancy xi) juicy xii) racism

C i) plague ii) league iii) catalogue iv) dialogue v) vague vi) intrigue
vii) colleague viii) vogue

Revise comparatives and superlatives (page 9)

1

Descriptor	Comparative	Superlative
tall	taller	tallest
angry	angrier	angriest
mean	meaner	meanest
dark	darker	darkest
long	longer	longest
hard	harder	hardest

2 a) slowest, faster b) younger, oldest c) lighter, heaviest d) cheaper

More prefixes (pages 10–11)

A Answers will vary
ambivalent, audio, contrary, extract, foretell, hypersensitive, microwave,
monotonous, octave, photosensitive, primitive, telegraph

1 a) forecast b) hypercritical c) photosensitive d) contraband
e) audition f) monogamy or monogamous

2 b) distant seeing = TV
c) stones falling apart = collapsing
d) both hands = neither left- nor right-handed
e) all powerful = complete power
f) distant seeing = instrument for seeing far

3 Answers will vary
monodextrous = using one hand

Foreign plurals, foreign suffixes (pages 12–13)

A Answers will vary
terminus, antenna, stadium, plateau

B Answers will vary
monograph, xenophobia, theology, stethoscope

1 a) termini b) plateaux c) tumuli d) antennae e) stadia f) addenda

2 a) small seeing = instrument for seeing small things
b) light writing = image on paper c) self writing = signature
d) everything feared = fear of everything e) crime study = study of crime

3 a) beautiful writing b) seeing beautiful things c) fear of water
d) fear of spiders

Suffix -ance, -ence (pages 14–15)

A ignorance, abundance, resonance, ascendance, attendance,
brilliance, compliance; confidence, decadence, coherence, indulgence,
convergence, divergence, emergence

1 -ance: reluctance, elegance, fragrance, assistance, reliance, arrogance,
significance, attendance, constance, repugnance
-ence: insolence, innocence, recurrence, difference, excellence, presence,
prudence, competence, patience, diligence

2 a) combatant b) communicant c) defendant d) descendant
e) applicant f) disputant

3 a) dependent, dependant b) attendant, attendance
c) respondent, correspondence d) confidant, confidence
e) defendant, defence

Suffix -ery, -ory, -ary (pages 16–17)

A -ery: machinery, misery, nursery
-ory: compulsory, memory, satisfactory, category
-ary: tributary, February, military, dictionary, anniversary, library, burglary

1 -ary: summary, anniversary, secondary, military, library
-ery: discovery, gallery, joinery, celery, mystery
-ory: satisfactory, dormitory, lavatory, memory, factory

2 a) bakery b) secretary c) voluntary d) territory e) history
f) brewery g) temporary

3 a) nursery, primary b) January, February
c) stationery, stationary d) compulsory, voluntary
e) monastery, cemetery f) bakery, surgery

Revise suffix -le, -el, -al (pages 18–19)

A Answers will vary
devil, fossil, gerbil, lentil, tonsil, weevil; carol, Bristol, gambol,
Mongol, petrol, symbol

1 -al: decimal, cannibal, scandal, rascal, pedal
-le: amiable, puddle, pimple, tentacle, cradle
-el: rebel, tassel, panel, barrel, tunnel

2 a) ankle b) quarrel c) hospital d) nettle e) bicycle
f) camel g) cupful

3 a) idol, idle b) bridal, bridle c) principal, principle
d) meddle, medal e) mussels, muscles

Revise suffix -er, -or, -ar (pages 20–21)

A i) honorable, vigorous ii) metrical, theatrical

1 baker, hammer, traitor, burglar, beggar, victor, major, river, pillar

2 a) tractor b) actor c) dollar d) colour e) armour f) visitor g) butcher

3 a) miner, minor b) cellar, seller c) hangar, hanger
d) friar, fryer e) censor, sensor

Vocabulary: antonyms (pages 22–23)

A unable, defrost, distaste, misplace, anticlockwise, nonsense, incapable

B i) hopeless ii) careless iii) mindless iv) topless v) clueless vi) fatless

1 Answers will vary
a) anti-smoker is against smoking b) non-smoker doesn't smoke
c) ex-smoker used to smoke d) move away e) lose f) substitute

2 crouch, leap; lose, find; blacken, whiten; uninterested, fascinated;
disinterested, biased; steam, ice; solidify, liquefy; strengthen, weaken;
rapidly, sluggishly

3 Answers will vary
a) dull b) minimum c) freezing d) gradually e) coy
f) couch potato g) floor

Spelling rule: i before e (pages 24–25)

1 receipt, deceit; conceive, perceive; their, heir; tied, cried; either, neither;
chief, thief; fierce, pierce; patient, ancient; yield, field

2 pieced, priest; grief, leaf; eight, state; reign, stain; pier, fear; view, new;
friend, bend; field, pealed; their, mare

3 a) niece b) handkerchief c) ceiling d) receipt e) eight f) height g) siege

Revise stress in words (page 27)

1 forgotten, forbidden, cancelled, travelled, signalled, trumpeted,
levelled, visited

2 transference, beginning, cancellation, abandonment, limitation,
permission, preference

3 a) cancelled, visiting b) signalled, travelling
c) galloped, abandoning d) entered, referred
e) regretted, forgotten f) labelled, parcelling

47

Silent syllables (pages 28–29)

A Answers will vary

chocolates, 2, o; lavatory, 3, o; secretary, 3, a; extraordinary, 4, a; comfortable, 3, or; temperature, 3, e; literature, 3, e; interesting, 3, e; every, 2, e; valuable, 3, a; sovereign, 2, e

1 review, ancient; weird, pierce; bone, late; observatory, laboratory; diamonds, chocolates; comfortable, secretary; extraordinary, indefatigable

2 **a)** parliament **b)** valuable **c)** diamonds **d)** February **e)** government **f)** ancient **g)** science **h)** mystery

3 vegetables, laboratory, decorative, Parliament, ordinarily

Making verbs (pages 30–31)

A These -en root words are all adjectives; these -ise and -ify root words are all nouns; these -ate verbs are root words themselves.

1 lessen, fatten, redden, coarsen, cheapen, blacken, whiten, broaden, widen, quicken

2 colonise, demonise, digitise, energise, motorise, televise, theorise, beautify, classify, identify, quantify

3 **a)** equalise, moralise, simplify, solidify, localise, maximise, minimise, purify **b)** liquidise, liquidate, liquefy

Making nouns (pages 32–33)

A -ness, all adjectives; -ility, all adjectives; -ism, all adjectives; -tion, all verbs

1 fatness, redness, coarseness, cheapness, blackness, whiteness, quickness

2 flexibility, vulnerability, sensibility, changeability, feasibility, enjoyability, legibility, reliability

3 addition, subtraction, multiplication, division, fractions, question, exclamation; divison, ending -sion

Vocabulary: synonyms (pages 34–35)

A Answers will vary

Adjectives: shiny / polished; tall / lofty; jagged / spiky; soft / gentle; sharp / pointed

Verb participles: plodding / trudging; crawling / shuffling; racing / tearing; leaping / jumping

Verbs past tense: said / uttered; shouted/yelled; whispered / muttered; announced / reported; replied / answered

Adverbs: slowly / sluggishly; loudly / deafeningly; suddenly / quickly; quietly / softly

Prepositions: near / close; beside / next; below / under; above / over; behind / beyond

Nouns: thief / robber; granny / grandma; assistant / helper; official / dignitary

1 darting, racing; brilliantly, wonderfully; harsh, hard; softly, quietly; loud, deafening; snoozing, dozing; trudging, plodding

2 Answers will vary

b) walking, marching, running **c)** small, medium, large **d)** slow, average, bright **e)** hungry, peckish, full

3 **a)** patients **b)** pensioners **c)** supporters **d)** babies **e)** assistants

Using a thesaurus (page 37)

1 **a)** bold, blue **b)** black small capitals **c)** bold, black **d)** black, roman **e)** black, italic

2 **a)** 1 noun **b)** 3 verbs **c)** 2 adjectives **d)** because it is harder to find synonyms for naming words.

3 **a)** fold, twist, buckle **b)** lean, bow, stoop, crouch **c)** They're all different word classes. **d)** faith, creed, religion **e)** faster, more effectively

Homophones (pages 38–39)

A ceiling / sealing: noun / verb; it's / its: verb, adjective; miner / minor: noun, adjective; medal / meddle: noun / verb; pedal / peddle: noun / verb; rough / ruff: adjective / noun; throne / thrown: noun / verb

1 Answers will vary

a) I passed the gate. **b)** That happened in the past. **c)** That was in past times. **d)** I ran past the gate. **e)** She flew past.

2 Answers will vary

a) I drive a fast car. **b)** I am fasting for Lent. **c)** The car goes fast. **d)** I need less time. **e)** I sing less these days. **f)** That is the lesser evil.

3 Answers will vary

a) That is a kind compliment. **b)** I compliment you on your writing. **c)** Mustard is a complement to beef. **d)** And the beef complements the mustard.

Informal and formal vocabulary (pages 40–41)

A Answers will vary

Informal: in the playground; to your friends; I'm off.

Formal: in the classroom; to your teacher; May I go outside?

1 Answers will vary

g8 = great

2 **a)** should not **b)** must not **c)** will not **d)** shall not **e)** we will **f)** he had

3 said: alleged, claimed, reported, reckoned

then: subsequently, thereafter, consequently

love from: yours sincerely, yours faithfully

Vocabulary: standard English (page 42)

A **i)** me **ii)** I **iii)** I **iv)** I

B **i)** they are **ii)** shall not **iii)** great **iv)** and **v)** avenue **vi)** minute or minimum **vii)** maximum **viii)** anonymous

C Answers will vary

i) I didn't see anybody at the park. **ii)** I don't want anything from the shop. **iii)** She can't make friends with anybody. **iv)** Make sure you don't get into any trouble.

Idioms and colloquialisms (page 43)

A Answers will vary

i) hurry up **ii)** kind of, a bit **iii)** when you really want something **iv)** having a problem **v)** when you can't make a decision and want both **vi)** somebody I really love **vii)** a good luck tradition **viii)** drive somebody mad **ix)** tell somebody's secret **x)** a really small room **xi)** asking somebody to stop

B Answers will vary

We were supposed to be going for a walk but it was raining heavily so we decided to stay inside instead. I was very disappointed and said I hoped the weather would improve. But Dad said, 'There is very little chance of that happening!'

Word list for Years 5 and 6 (page 44)

2

haras	harass	harrass
occupy	occupie	ocupy
stomack	stomac	stomach
achieeve	achieve	acheive
professhun	professian	profession
reconise	recognyse	recognise
community	communitey	comunity
pregidice	prejudice	prejudis

3 Answers will vary

a) Please can I have your signature on this cheque?

b) I would recommend the restaurant on the corner.

c) According to Dad, I can have anything I want for my birthday.

d) As a Year 6 privilege, you can wear silver jumpers!

The Spelling Test (page 45)

1 **a)** 5 **b)** 5 **c)** 4 **d)** 5 **e)** 6 **f)** 4

2 I've been benefiting from travelling around the circumference of the globe; I've visited many countries in Europe, and crossed many bridges. Now I'm back home and putting my feet up by the hearth.

3 Answers will vary

a) boiling, warm **b)** freezing, chilly **c)** damp, moist **d)** parched, not rainy

Vocabulary: compound words (page 46)

1 rainbow, teapot, peanut, ponytail, suitcase

2 newspaper, headache, strawberry, footprint, stopwatch, toothbrush

3 Answers will vary

a) I love walking through the countryside.

b) They laughed throughout the whole film.

c) They can look after themselves.

d) The headquarters were hidden behind a secret door.